SAME OR DIFFERENT?

Draw a circle around each of the 2 things that are the **same**.

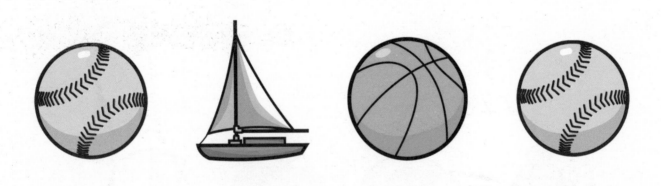

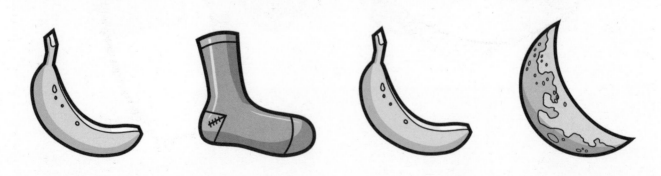

Color the things that are the **same**.

3

Draw a circle around each of the 2 things that are the **same**.

Color the things that are the **same**.

Which are the SAME?

Draw a circle around each of the 2 shapes that are the **same**.

Color the shapes that are the **same**.

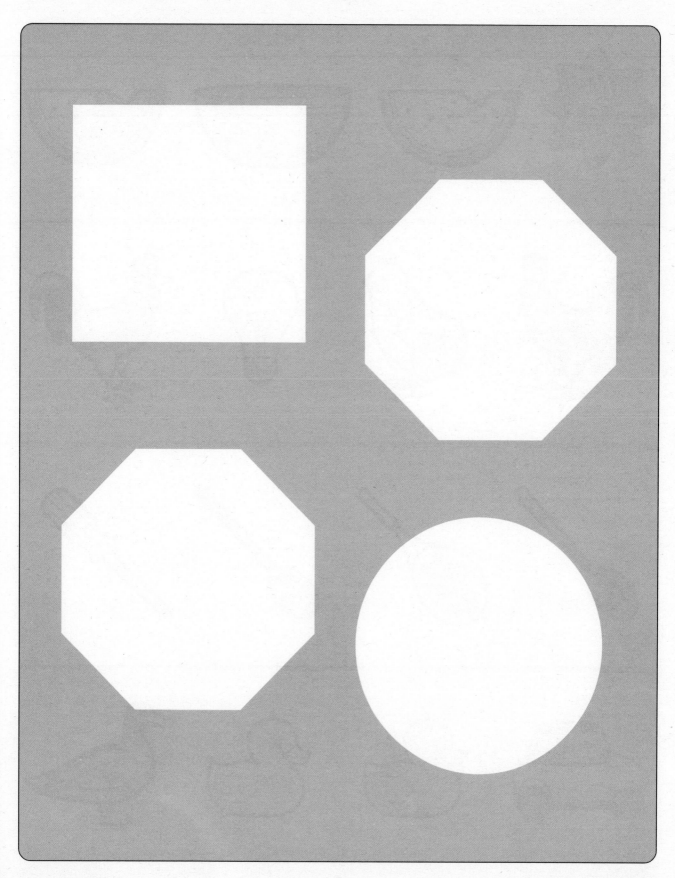

Draw a circle around each of the 2 things that are the **same**.

Color the things that are the **same**.

9

Draw a circle around each of the 2 things that are the **same**.

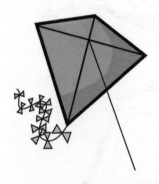   

Color the things that are the **same**.

Draw a circle around each of the 2 letter pairs that are the **same**.

QI FR ZU QI

DT CB DT LO

MH AB GR AB

VJ KY VJ IC

Color the letters that are the **same**.

Which are the SAME size?

Draw a circle around each of the 2 things that are the **same size**.

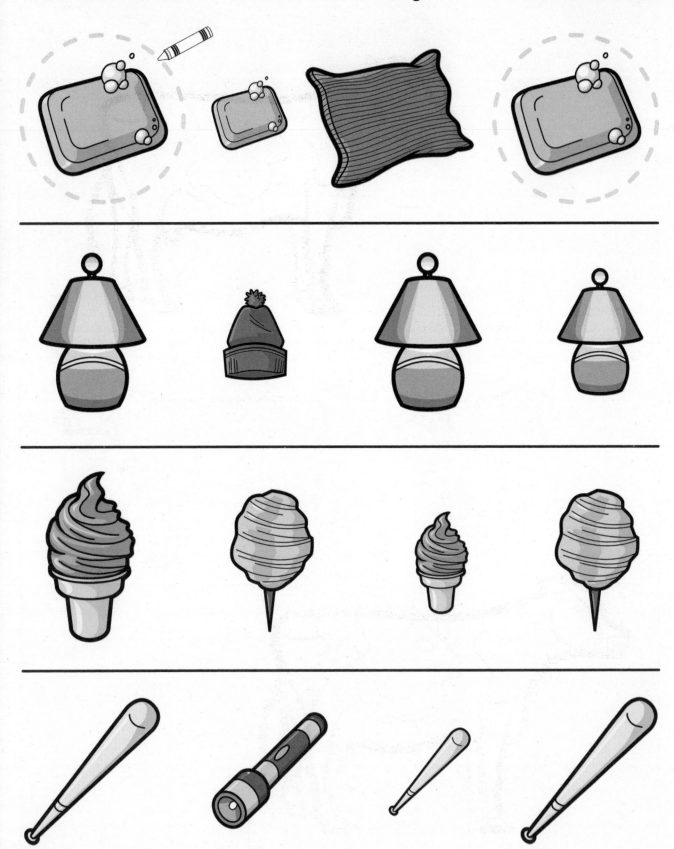

Color the things that are the **same size**.

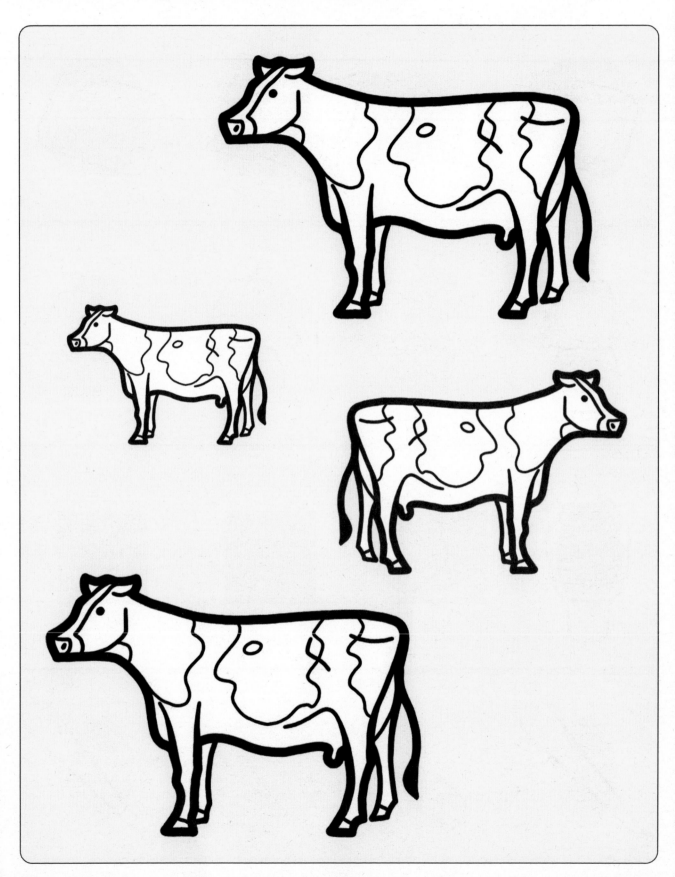

Draw a circle around the shape that is **different**.

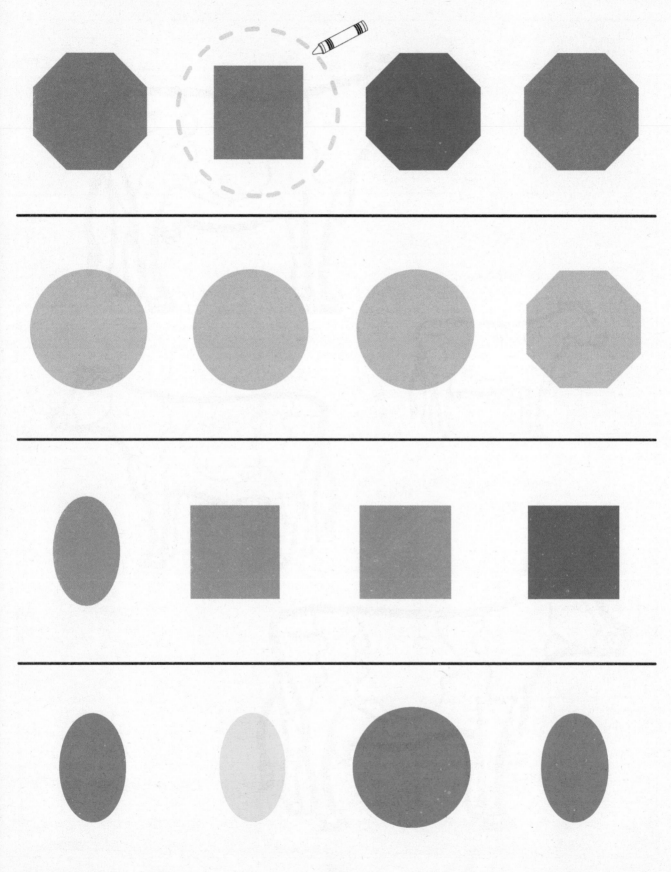

Color the shape that is **different**.

Draw a circle around the thing that is **different**.

Color the thing that is **different**.

19

Draw a circle around the thing that is **different**.

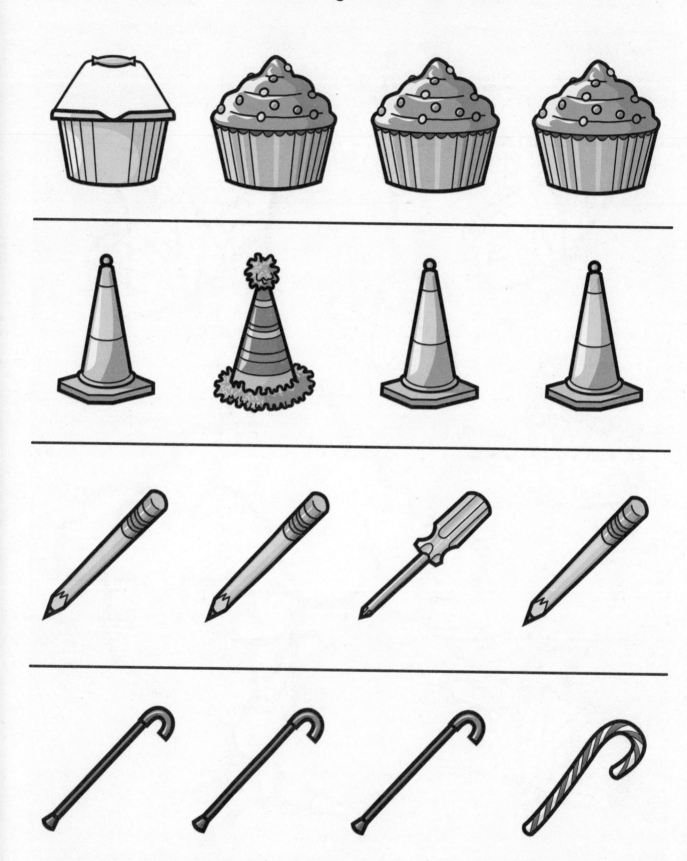

Color the thing that is **different**.

Draw a circle around the thing that is **different**.

Color the thing that is **different**.

Draw a circle around the letter pair that is **different**.

CJ   GI   CJ   CJ

KO   KO   KO   GT

RS   RS   PR   RS

LE   TE   TE   TE

Color the letter that is **different**.

Which is a DIFFERENT size?

Draw a circle around the thing that is a **different size**.

Color the thing that is a **different size**.

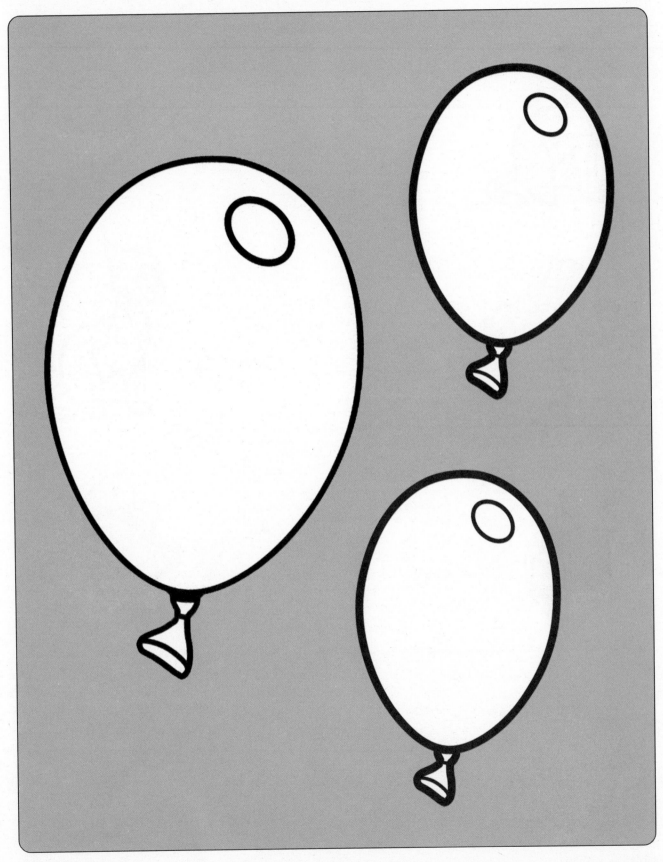

Draw lines to match up the things that are the **same**.

Draw lines to match up the shapes that are the **same**.

29

What is the SAME? What is DIFFERENT?

Look at each block. Notice the colors, sizes, and types of objects, food, or animals. What is the **same**? What is **different**? (There can be many answers.)

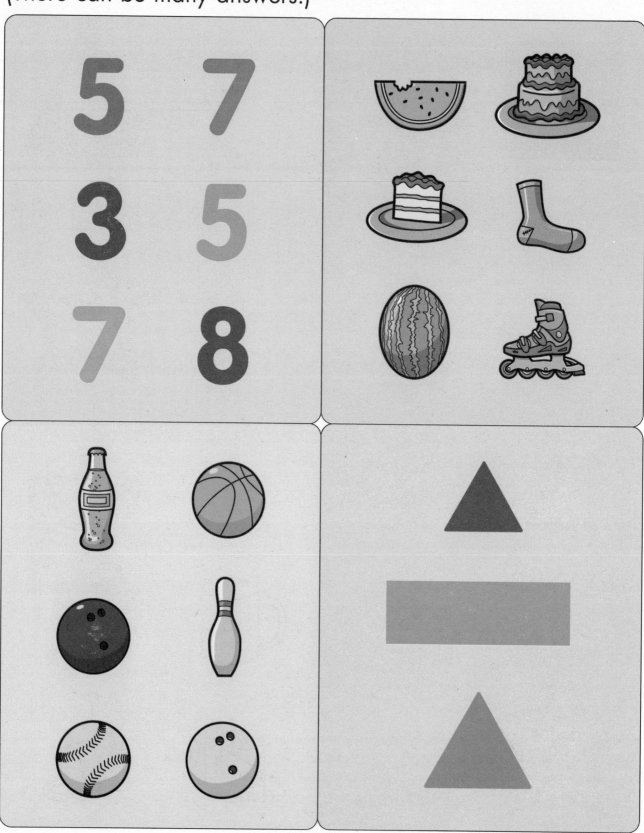

What is the **same**? What is **different**?

Fun Family Activities

The following activities will provide additional review of the concepts explored on the workbook pages.

1. Memory Game

Using two identical decks of playing cards, select matching pairs of cards. For first-time players, begin with 10 pairs of cards. As the child becomes accustomed to playing and his or her attention span increases, add additional pairs of cards.

Game Directions: This game can be played by 1 or more players. The goal of the game is to collect pairs of cards that are the same. Mix up the cards and spread them face down on a table. Player #1 turns over two cards. If they match, the player keeps the cards and takes another turn. If the cards do not match they are turned back over. When Player #1 does not make a match the play passes to Player #2. The game continues with each player taking a turn until all the cards have been matched. The player with the most pairs wins.

2. Classification

Take a walk to hunt for fallen leaves. Help the child sort the leaves into categories. For example, some may look like mittens, some may have pointed edges, some may have rounded edges, etc.

3. Sorting Game

Look for sorting opportunities in your everyday life. Ask the child to sort silverware into like groups. How many groups are there? Ask the child to describe how the groups were made. Are the large spoons with the small spoons, or did your child choose to make a separate grouping based on size?

4. Block Party

While playing with colored blocks, help the child sort the blocks by size, shape, and color. For example, select all the large blocks, the large red blocks, the small blue blocks, etc.

5. Travel Game

As you and the child travel on errands, look for things that are the same or different. Depending on what criteria you use, two items could be considered either the same or different. For example, two red cars might be the same because they are both red, or they might be different because one is large and one is small. Each time you play, be sure to determine the characteristics that make things the same or different.

Illustrations by
Greg Hardin

6. Reward Stickers

Use reward stickers to celebrate a job well done. You or the child can choose when to place a sticker on a specific page. Use a sticker as a reward when the child completes a page that requires extra care or is a little more difficult. The child can choose to place stickers on pages he or she is proud of completing.